This book was made possible by the support of our generous donors. Thank you for helping us honor the life and work of Dr. Ananthi Jebasingh.

Ananthi's Advocates
with a gift of $1000 or more:

Jess and Angela Correll
Preston and Rachel Correll
Dale and Louisa Ditto
Joel and Amanda Lang
Paul and Judy Lerwick
Robert and Leslie Littrell
Patton and Laura Marie Thompson
Centenary United Methodist Church
Lookout Mountain Presbyterian Church
Matthew 23:35 Foundation
The Generosity Trust

Sadie's Samaritans
with a gift of $500:

Andy and Anna Melvin
Bob and Julie Mudd
Charles and Patty Renfroe

Sunny's Supporters
with a gift of $250:

David and Maribeth Burton
Krista Clements
Dan and Mary Lewis
Hugh and Nancy Maclellan
Chas and Lindsey Perry
Tim and Susan Philpot
Errol and Karen Rohr
Servants' Servant Ministry

Sadie
and the School
that LOVE Built

Written by Amanda Evans Lang

Illustrated by Mandy Newham-Cobb

Sadie was enjoying her time at the Good Samaritan School in India. She found so many ways to be helpful. Sadie started every day in Morning Assembly. She led the pledges and sang silly songs with all the children.

After assembly, she headed to the science lab where she supervised experiments and science reports.

Then she went to the field for her cricket lesson.

Next was music, where Sadie was learning to play the Sitar..

Some days she helped in art or read outloud in the library.

Before she knew it, it was time to drive the bus home.

When she was not helping at the school, Sadie explored India eager to see everything. She climbed mountains, bathed elephants, and danced with monkeys.

She learned to charm snakes and rode a train all the way to the Indian Ocean.

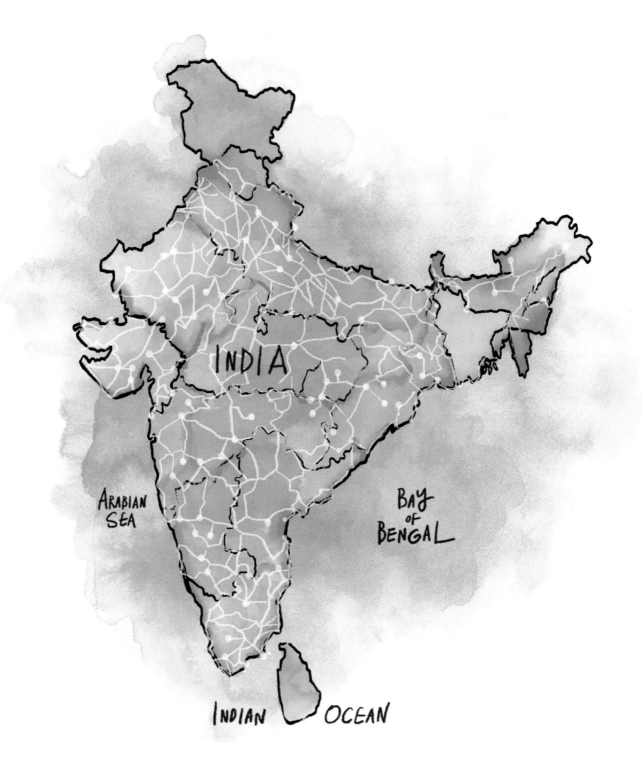

Sadie went to the markets and shopped for
beautiful saris, incense, and delicious spices. She
wrote letters to her friends about all of her
adventures and collapsed in her bed each night
delighted about everything she was experiencing in India.

One day Mummy-ji, the head of the school, invited
Sadie to tea to meet a special vistor.
While they drank tea and waited for him to arrive,
Sadie told Mummy-ji about all of her adventures.

"Mummy-ji, there are so many things to see,
taste, and explore in India!"

Mummy-ji had lived in
India her whole life and Sadie
thought that she must have had
a GAGILLION adventures.

Sadie wondered what had been
Mummy-ji's
GREATEST ADVENTURE.

Had she climbed all the way to
the top of Himalayan
Mountains?
Or been across the
desert in a caravan of camels?

Had she wrestled a tiger?

"What is the most exciting thing YOU have ever done?" asked Sadie.

Mummy-ji thought for a minute and said,
"I will tell you about my greatest
adventure, while we wait!"

"When I moved to Delhi, I was just like you,
Sadie. My heart longed to do something kind
and exciting. My husband traveled for his work
and my three children were in school.

One morning as I was cleaning up from
breakfast, I heard a knock at the door.
When I answered the door, there was a very
little boy asking for something to eat. I gave
him everything left from breakfast and watched
him cross a busy road to go back to his home."

"The next day, he came again and before
long I was saving food for him every morning.

One morning, I heard the usual knock at
the door... but I was shocked to open the
door to a crowd of children. They said, 'hamei bhook
lag rahi hain', which means *we are hungry* in Hindi."

"I got so angry...and sent them away!

I wanted to help the little boy because he was hungry and did not have enough to eat, but I did not want to make him a beggar."

Mummy-ji explained, "In India, many, many children live in very small homes in neighborhoods called slums. They do not always have everything the children need. The homes are so small that they do not have a kitchen, bathroom, or sometimes even electricity. The whole family lives in one room and the children sleep on mats on the ground. It is hard to get clean water for drinking or cooking and it is easy to get sick."

"Many parents do not have enough money to pay for all the things that they need to live a good life. Children try to help their family by finding ways to get more money instead of being able to learn in school. They will try to sell food on a street corner or sometimes they even have to beg."

"I did not want the children to spend their time begging so I sent them away thinking that I was not really helping them. As soon as I closed the door, I heard a small voice tell me that I had made a mistake. I wanted to do something helpful and kind with my life...and there at my door had stood the chance to help many children."

"All I could do was hope the little boy would come back. Every morning I waited with food that I had saved for him... but he did not come back."

"You must have been so sad!",
Sadie said to Mummy-ji.

"I was so sad", said Mummy-ji, remembering how she had longed for a second chance to help him.

"But just when I had given up, I heard a knock on the door. I rushed to the door and there was the little boy! I told him how sorry I was for getting angry and asked for his forgiveness.

He was eager and hungry, so we worked out a deal that if he came every morning, we would have a lesson and I would give him something to eat."

"The day Sunny learned to write his name, he danced around my living room. I danced with him!"

"Before long, Sunny's neighbors wanted to learn to read and write, too. And then mothers began bringing their young children to my door asking for admission to my school, begging me to keep their children safe while they worked as laborers or at the market. I tried to tell them that I did not have a school … but I could not turn the children away. Before long, the garage and verandah were overflowing with children hungry to learn.

Soon there were more children than I could fit in my whole apartment and even more children wanted to come to my school. I had to do something!"

"The children had to travel across a busy road to get to my apartment from their homes, so I thought that we should have school right where they lived. I went to the man in charge of the slum and asked if there was anywhere we could have school. I was so happy when he told me that he had just the place!

In the middle of the slum, there was a room where people without homes slept at night. The room was between two large bathrooms, each with 100 toilets.The entire neighborhood shared these bathrooms and came here every day."

"THE TOILET COMPLEX!

I did not want to teach school in the TOILET COMPLEX,
but I remembered that little voice that told me
I could show love to these children by teaching right
where they lived... So much love had been
shown to me, and I could not
even think about saying no!"

"By then, I had to find more teachers to teach so many children. Every morning, we would scrub the floors and make the toilet complex as nice as we could before the children came to learn. We hung flowers and used fans to help with the smell and heat.

The children named the school the toilet school and were so happy to be learning. The parents were happy that the children were safe while they worked and no one complained about the smell. So many children came that we had to have morning and afternoon school.

I was so happy to be teaching and helping so many children that I could never imagine we would have bigger things to come."

"One day, the slum commissioner told me that they would be tearing down the whole neighborhood and the families would have to move to another part of the city. Our toilet school would be torn down, too."

"We put up tents on the streets, and for years, we had school every day, rain or shine, morning and afternoon. Even though there were many people living around us that did not have good homes, and so many were hungry and sick, our school was full of love and hope.

My heart was so happy that so many children could learn and make a better life for themselves, but I wanted a real school for them. The children came to school when it was stinky, rainy, and crowded. They wanted to learn so badly. I knew that they deserved a better school."

I wrote many letters and traveled all across the world to tell everyone who would listen about how much the children wanted to go to learn and needed a real school. I made plans and found a place to build. I went to the government offices almost every day and told them about the real school we wanted to build.

Finally, there was a miracle! Enough people came together to build the Good Samaritan School!"

"Children around the world had collected change and told their parents about their hope for the children of India. Parents had told their own friends. Grown-ups wrote letters and found others who would help. So many people came together to raise the money we needed and the goverment of India gave us permission to build a real school."

Mummy-ji took Sadie by the hand and as they walked through the beautiful school building she said to Sadie,

"THIS has been
my greatest
adventure!

I tried to make life better for one little boy by giving him all the love that I had been shown...and look what happened!"

"LOVE built a real school for
so many children."

"Now I want you to meet Sunny!

When he was a very little boy, he taught me that one small act of

LOVE

can change everything."

As Sadie and Mummy-ji finished their tea, Sadie took a deep breath as she let Mummy-ji's story rush over her.

She was so excited to have met Sunny and heard the story of how the Good Samaritan School began but one thing still bothered her.

"Mummy-ji, I don't think I will ever do anything as brave as you,"
Sadie whispered.

Mummy-ji looked deep into Sadie's eyes and placed her hand on Sadie's heart. "You already are! The LOVE that built this school is the same LOVE that lives in your heart. That LOVE brought you all the way to India and to us at the Good Samaritan School."

"Love is not finished here, Sadie,
and neither is our adventure!"

Made in the USA
Monee, IL
10 September 2022

13685584R10026